THE BADDIES

Lord and
Lady Evil

Dr Y

They want to rule the galaxy.

THE GOODIES

Boo Hoo   Jet   Tip

They want to stop them.

"I can't believe that you are scared
of spiders," said Jet.
"Believe it. I am!" said Tip.
Jet shook her head. "Spiders can't do
you any harm..."

11

The call continued, "We have crashed on Planet Arakno. We need your help! Please rescue us!"

"Let's go!" said Jet

15

"What is the matter?" asked Jet.

"I spy a spider!" said Tip.

"Not again!" laughed Jet. "Are you scared of a little spider?"

"No! I am scared of a great big one! And its friends!"

17

19

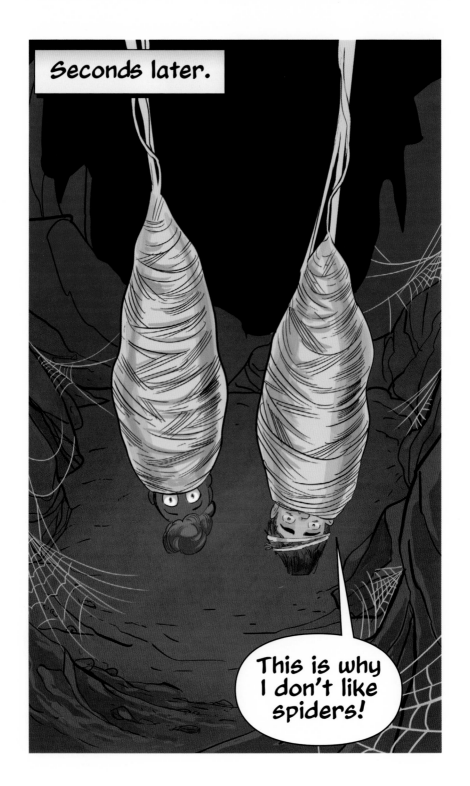

" 'Spiders can't do you any harm!' Ha!" said Tip.

"Can't you put a more positive spin on this?" said Jet.

"We are going to die!" said Tip. "What is there to be positive about!"

"I have contacted Boo Hoo 2. She is my sister," said Boo Hoo.

"You have a sister?" asked Jet.

"We have the same motherboard," replied Boo Hoo. "She is bringing a vacuum cleaner."

"What good will that do?" cried Tip.

"Wait and see," said Boo Hoo. "Take my hands."